The Story of Prince Bladud

A Tale of Bath

By Jane Samson

This book is dedicated to Barney.

Thanks to Josie, Gill, Judy, Lily, Austin and all my family, friends and animals.

This book belongs to:

ISAAIK

Before the Romans came to
Britain, Iron Age people lived
in Iron Age forts.
Prince Bladud lived in this one, with
his mother, his father, all of his friends
and all of his devoted animals.

This is where he slept.

Until the day he woke up feeling very poorly
and covered from head to foot with big red spots.

Everyone was worried.
What should they do?

"Begone!"

They didn't want to catch his spots,
so they blew their trumpets and sent him away.

He walked and he walked...

and he walked

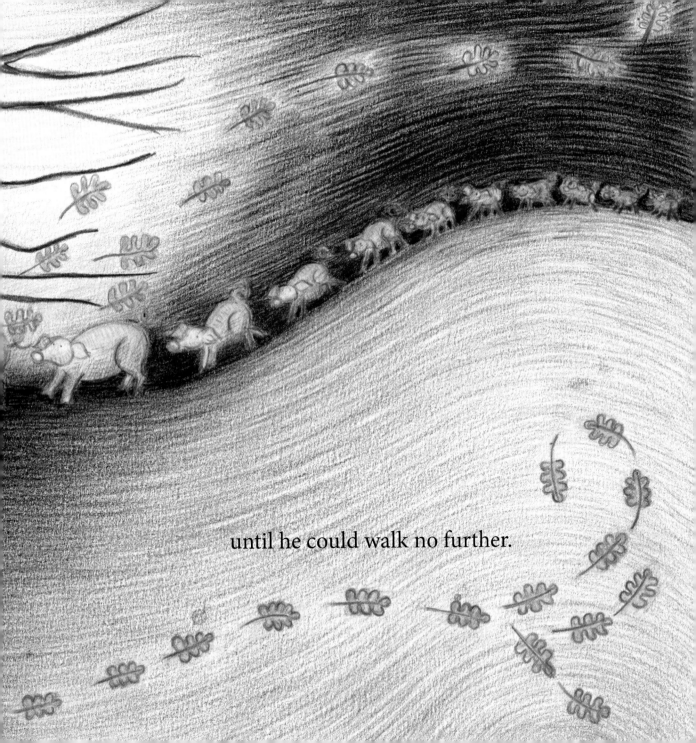

until he could walk no further.

A kind old woman gave him some pigs.
She told him to look for acorns
because that's what pigs love to eat.

He took them to the woods and built a shelter
to keep them warm and dry.
But they got poorly too and caught his spots!
What could Bladud do?

Early next morning, Bladud woke with a plan.
"Shhh...." he whispered, "Follow me!"

They ran as fast as they could - but their spots caught up with them.
"Lets look for acorns." said Bladud. "That will cheer us up."

"Acorns!" cried the pigs.

"Oh what lovely mud!"

?

Spotless!

How happy they all were to be well again!
Bladud could go home at last.

When Bladud became king
he went back to that magic place
and built a shrine to Sulis Minerva,
the goddess of water...

in the place
we now call Bath.